Standalone Power Generation

LAP LAMBERT Academic Publishing

Imprint
Any brand names and product names mentioned in this book are subject to trademark, brand or patent protection and are trademarks or registered trademarks of their respective holders. The use of brand names, product names, common names, trade names, product descriptions etc. even without a particular marking in this work is in no way to be construed to mean that such names may be regarded as unrestricted in respect of trademark and brand protection legislation and could thus be used by anyone.

Cover image: www.ingimage.com

Publisher:
LAP LAMBERT Academic Publishing
is a trademark of
International Book Market Service Ltd., member of OmniScriptum Publishing Group
17 Meldrum Street, Beau Bassin 71504, Mauritius
Printed at: see last page
ISBN: 978-3-659-89781-8

Zugl. / Approved by: Ahmedabad, Gujarat Technological Univesity, Diss., 2015

Jeegnasha Asodariya
Viranchi Pandya

Standalone Power Generation

Table of Contents

LIST OF FIGURES

LIST OF TABLES

LIST OF ABBREVIATIONS

AC	Alternating Current
ADC	Analogue to Digital Converter
CCM	Continuous Conduction Mode
CIDBI	Coupled Inductor and Double Boost Topology
CMOS	Complementary metal-oxide-Semiconductor
CPU	Central Processing Unit
DC	Direct Current
DCM	Dis-continuous Conduction Mode
DG	Distributed Power Generation
DSO	Digital Storage Oscilloscope
DSP	Digital Signal Processor
ePWM	Enhanced Pulse Width Modulation
EVM	Event Manager Module
FPU	Floating point Unit
GPIO	General Purpose Input Output
HCI	Hybrid Cascade Inverter
HF	High Frequency
HRPWM	High Resolution Pulse Width Modulation
HV	High Voltage
IDE	Integrated Development Environment
JTAG	Joint Test Action Group
MAC	Multiply-Accumulate
PLL	Phase Locked Loop
PWM	Pulse Width Modulation
PV	Photovoltaic
SPWM	Sinusoidal Pulse Width Modulation
THD	Total Harmonic Distortion

STAND ALONE POWER GENERATION MODULE

Submitted By

Jeegnasha D. Asodariya (130010741004)

ABSTRACT

Photovoltaic (PV) power generation is increasing day by day so that highly efficient and low cost pure sine wave inverters are required. This report explores a topology for photovoltaic inverter for stand-alone application. The three basic types of PV inverters are centralized inverter, string inverter and module integrated/module oriented inverters. There exist different topologies related to single phase micro inverters which are widely used in industrial applications. Micro inverter is the best topology among all the three PV invertes. Fly back based micro inverter employs Fly back converter, and filter circuit and unfolder. The switching technique of proposed inverter consists with a combination of sinusoidal pulse width modulation (SPWM), which is generated by using sinusoidal wave and triangular wave. Overall performance of this inverter is simulated through the Pspice software. The results of simulation are shown. Then isolated full bridge based micro inverter is also simulated through Pspice software. The detailed technical analysis is also shown. SPWM gives better results by using DSP TMS320F28335 via MATLAB-CCS 3.3 connection. Proposed inverter topology includes full bride inverter circuit with SPWM as gate drive pulses, which is very simple and efficient. It may be able to meet the challenges of power crises in rural areas.

CHAPTER 1 INTRODUCTION

1.1 Background

The demand of energy is increasing day by day so the search of energy sources is required which are cost efficient. The sun is source of renewable energy which offers unlimited energy. Connection of Photovoltaic modules for generation of power is very environmental friendly and efficient. The PV modules include several solar cells, which convert the solar energy directly into electrical energy. They are connected as to provide desired levels of DC current and voltage. They produce electricity because of a quantum mechanical process known as the "photovoltaic effect" (PV). The PV systems has disadvantages like high cost and low efficiency compared to the conventional sources like fossil fuels.[16],[17].

Power semiconductor devices are the heart of the present power electronics. They are widely used in power electronic converters in the form of a matrix of on or off switches, and used to convert one form of power to another. There are four basic conversion tasks that normally can be applied such as AC to AC, AC to DC, DC to AC and DC to DC. Inverter is one of the converters which are called DC to AC converter. It converts DC power to AC power to a symmetric AC output voltage at desired magnitude (220 Volts) and frequency (50 Hz). Inverter is broadly used in industrial applications like variable speed AC motor drives, induction heating, stand-alone power supplies and uninterruptible power supplies. The DC power input of inverter is achieved from the existing power supply network. It can be a battery, photovoltaic, wind energy, fuel cell or other DC sources.

1.2 Motivation

Inverter is power conversion technique which is used to convert DC input voltage to AC output voltage. The waveforms of perfect inverters i.e. output voltage and current must be sinusoidal. But the waveform of practical inverter is not sinusoidal and contains harmonics. Then, for this project, it should be closer to sinusoidal waveform within +- 5% harmonics contains. Harmonic contents in inverter output depends more to number of pulses per cycle. Square wave switching method will give more harmonic contents in inverter output compared to sinusoidal pulse width modulation switching technique. This is because of number of pulses per cycle of pulse width modulation can be modified on the frequency of triangular carrier waveform. The frequency of triangular waveform can be modified from lower frequency to higher frequency. If the frequency of triangular wave is high then the number of pulses per cycle also increased and at the same time it will decrease the harmonic contents of the inverter. The high switching technique will increase power losses and it also needs to take care while the inverter switching designs. The following issues are needed to be considered in order to meet the requirement of inverter.

i. Cost of equipment

ii. Size of filter

iii. Total harmonic distortion (THD)

iv. Power loss in switching elements (MOSFETs, IGBTs, etc.)

To achieve the requirement of the inverter, the new switching technique, SPWM has been explored which is generated with combination of high frequency triangular wave and sine wave. Filter will provide a nearly constant output current and reduces THD generated by inverter.

1.3   Block diagram of power generation module

The block diagram represents the power generation module for stand-alone applications. Solar Panel's output voltage is given to DC-DC converter and then storage battery. Battery's output will be given to inverter (DC-AC) and then fed to the grid or load. The controlling mechanism is done by DSP module.

2

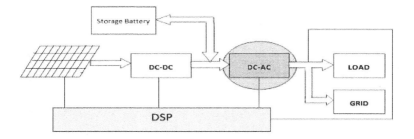

Figure 1.1 Block diagram of power generation module [11]

1.3.1 DC-DC boost converter

A Boost converter is DC to DC converter in which the output voltage is larger than the input voltage. It is also known as step up converter. Step up converter originates from step up transformer in which the input voltage is stepped up to a level higher than the input voltage. By law of conservation of energy, the input power is always equal to output power (by supposing no losses in the circuit).

$$\text{Input power } (P_{in}) = \text{Output power } (P_{out}) \tag{1.1}$$

As we know that $V_{in} < V_{out}$ in a boost converter, so that the output current is less than the input current. Therefore in boost converter

$$< V \quad \text{And} \quad > I \tag{1.2}$$

The operation of boost converter is that the inductor in the input circuit repels sudden deviations in input current. When switch is ON the inductor stores energy in the form of magnetic energy and discharges it when switch is opened. The capacitor in the output circuit is expected big sufficient so that the time constant of RC circuit in the output stage is high. The large time constant compared to switching period ensures a constant output voltage $V_o(t) = V_o$ (constant).

1.3.2 DC-AC converter (Inverter)

Inverter is one of power conversion device that widely used in the world to convert DC input voltage to AC output voltage. The output voltage waveforms of ideal

3

inverters should be sinusoidal. However, the waveform of practical inverter is non-sinusoidal and contains harmonics.

1.4   Objectives

The key points of this project can be given as:

- To design and implement switching technique for inverter, which are simple, consistent, low cost and highly efficient.
- Simulate the different topology for micro inverter by using power electronics simulation software, **Pspice** with different switching situations to get best performance.
- To develop gate pulse switching of inverter, SPWM is used which is combination of triangular wave and sinusoidal wave.
- To make a complete prototype of inverter with less than 300W power rating for PV application.
- To compare and examine the simulated results.
- To develop a laboratory prototype by using full bridge circuit and sinusoidal pulse width modulated (SPWM) as a gate drive pulses which is generated using DSP TMS320F28335.

1.5   Research methodology

The methods that will use to finish this thesis are illustrated through the flow chart shown in Fig.1.2:

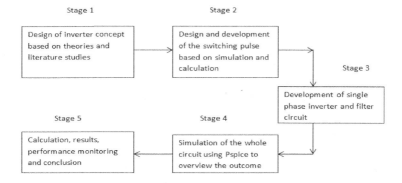

Figure 1.2 Research methodology

1.6   Organization of this report

The thesis consists of seven chapters. A short explanation is introduced here:

- **Chapter 1: Introduction**

This chapter discuss about the issue relating to the background of the thesis objectives, methodology and research structure.

- **Chapter 2: Literature review**

This chapter discusses mainly about PV array, different types of single phase PV inverter topologies, converter topology, and application. Some of literature regarding this thesis topic is also included in this chapter.

- **Chapter 3: Design and circuit analysis of fly back converter**

The Chapter 3 describes in detail the fly back converter, design value and the circuit analysis of the converter which includes the construction, design parameter, and waveforms

- **Chapter 4: Design and circuit analysis of isolated full bridge converter**

5

The chapter 4 describes in detail isolated full bridge converter, design value and the circuit analysis of the converter which includes the construction, design parameter, and waveforms.

- **Chapter 5: SPWM generation using DSP**

This chapter gives the basic idea of SPWM (sinusoidal pulse width modulation), generation of SPWM using DSP and specification of proposed DSP system with its features.

- **Chapter 6: Design of test prototype**

The chapter 6 will focus on complete hardware description about the proposed system, mainly to the simulation, method, results and implementation of proposed PV inverter related to the thesis topic.

- **Chapter 7: Conclusion and Future work**

Finally, a conclusion based on the obtained results is presented. It also includes suggestions for future work.

CHAPTER 2 LITERATURE REVIEW

2.1 Topologies of PV inverter

There are three basic PV inverter topologies namely centralized inverter, string inverter and module oriented/module integrated inverter.

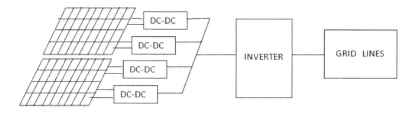

Figure 2. 1 Setup of centralized inverter [15]

In Centralized inverter, each solar panel has its own DC/DC converter to boost up the DC voltage coming out from panel. The output of all DC/DC converters is HV/DC (high voltage DC). HV/DC is fed to the centralized inverter and then to the grid.

The past equipment for PV inverter was based on centralized inverters which include the more numbers of PV panels joined into series. This structure will produce high voltage. To achieve high power levels, they were linked in parallel via string diodes.

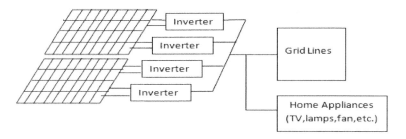

Figure 2. 2 Setup of string inverter [15]

String is made up of PV modules by connecting them in series. Output of the string is then given to an inverter. Isolated maximum power point tracking (MPPT) arrangement can be given to every string. By doing this arrangement, overall efficiency is improved compared to centralized inverter method and also there is reduction in price.

In String based inverter, Panels are linked to several inverters to acquire 120/240 V_{AC} at average power levels. The connection of inverter with the grid is shown in Fig 2.2. Here because of several inverters, they deliver higher power harvesting from solar panels. They also offer better system consistency.

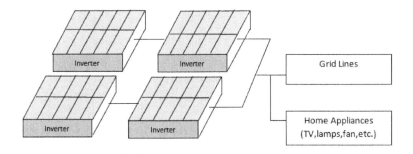

Figure 2. 3 Module oriented / Module integrated inverter [15]

In Module Oriented inverter, every solar panel unit has its private inverter. Module-oriented inverters are also known as micro inverters. A micro inverter system is shown in Fig 2.3. The integration of inverter and solar panel significantly decreases installation costs. It also maximizes the solar energy harvesting and improves safety.

2.2   Types of single phase inverters

There are two basic categories of single phase inverter as single stage inverter and multiple stage inverters. A single stage inverter is an inverter with only one stage of power conversion, which will boost up the input low dc voltage and converts that dc voltage to ac voltage. Depend on the number of switches used in inverter; single-phase inverters can be categorized as

1) four-switch topologies;

2) six-switch topologies.

In multiple-stage inverter, one or more stage will do the task of voltage step-up or step-down and last stage will do dc-ac conversion. Multiple stage inverters include more than one stage for power conversion. Multiple-stage inverters are categorized as

1) dc–dc–ac topologies (three stage);
2) dc–ac–dc–ac topologies (four stage);
3) dc–ac–ac topologies (three stage)

2.3 Literature review

M. Calais et al. [1] have given characterization of diverse sorts of PV inverters. Central inverters, with DC power ratings above 10 kW, suitable for PV framework arrangements with a few strings in parallel. When inverter outages, there were possibilities for generation of power losses. String inverters, which were intended for a framework arrangement of one string of PV modules. There were losses because of the mismatch of strings. Module integrated or module situated PV inverters with evaluated power underneath 500 W can be named a third group of PV inverters alongside central and string inverters.

S. B. Kjaer et al. [2] have given a survey on power inverter topologies for photovoltaic module. The power range for micro inverters were ordinarily inside of 90 Watts to 500 Watts, which covers the most commercial photovoltaic-modules. Self-commutated inverters are interchanged by the grid-commutated ones. As well as the bulky low-frequency transformers are also replaced by the high-frequency transformers, which are used for isolation as well as diminished size and enhanced efficiency.

Y. Xue, et al. [3] have proposed topologies of single-phase inverters in distributed power generation (DG) systems which comprise dc–ac conversion, yield power quality affirmation, different protection devices, and framework controls. Exclusive necessities for small distributed power generation systems incorporate ease, high efficiency and resistance for a greatly extensive variety of input voltage. These prerequisites have driven the inverter improvement toward less difficult topologies and structures, lower part tallies, and modular design. Both single-stage and different stage inverters have been created for power conversion in DG systems.

The review given by **Soeren Baekhoej Kjaer et al.** [4] focused on inverter technologies for connecting photovoltaic (PV) modules to a single-phase grid. Micro inverter can be classified on the basis of the number of power conversion steps in inverter; power decoupling type between PV module and grid; even the transformer is used or not. Several inverter topologies are given and evaluated with respect to demands, lifetime, component ratings, and cost.

The total power generation of PV array is decreased when few modules are partially covered by shadows. To overcome this drawback, **Toshihisa Shimizu et al.** [5] have given a fly back-type single phase utility interactive inverter for an AC module strategy. A small power DC-AC utility interactive inverter is mounted on each PV module individually. This inverter is used to generate the maximum power from its corresponding PV module.

S. B. Kjaer et al. [6] have given the novel topology which takes care of a important issue inside of the first topology: removal of leakage energy, without diminishing the efficiency and without influencing the method of operation. .Finally, an inverter has designed by utilizing the advanced tool, and the effectiveness was moved forward. The modified Shimizu inverter is a good solution for the micro inverter systems.

Abdel-Rahim, O. et al. [7] proposed a precise PV cell model which considers the environmental conditions, for example, temperature and shadow impacts. The structure consists of a one PV module; step up converter with high gain conversion ratio, and single phase inverter. It can be used at greater efficiency because it dodges the shadow impacts.

Power converter is the key component of the photovoltaic era framework. To enhance the energy transformation efficiency and accomplish a monetary solution, hybrid cascade inverter (HCI) is utilized by **Xiaonan Lu et al.** [11]. HCI has a comparable topology with ordinary H-bridge cascade inverter. HCI is a highly efficient inverter with low output harmonic components.

10

Erickson, R.W. et al. **[12]** proposed a Micro-inverter for Building-Integrated Photovoltaic. The photovoltaic modules get to be design components, requiring properties, for example, a low profile, simple connection with the grid system, and the capability to boost energy in a complex physical environment having shadows and reflections. These necessities of very low profile, high temperature, and high efficiency operation need considerable changes to the conventional inverter technologies for example comparatively low frequency CCM operation and electrolytic energy storage capacitors. DCM operation gives a practical solution by reducing both inductor value and switching loss.

Joshi, M. et al. **[13]** have given a highly efficient resonant solar micro-inverter. Resonant converters are an exceptional kind of forward converters offering the zero-voltage-switching and higher converter efficiency. They likewise have the benefits of less number of parts and sinusoidal currents and/or voltages in the circuit. The low voltage DC from the panel is converted to a rectified sinusoidal high-voltage DC using a resonant converter and a high-frequency transformer and a diode rectifier. This topology is very simple since it is based on the fast recovery diodes rather than the synchronous rectifiers.

A new module oriented inverter topology based on a fly back converter is presented by **Haibing Hu et al.** **[16].** The proposed fly back based topology includes a new power decoupling technique where large electrolytic capacitor are replaced by small film capacitor. Thus it will have a long life compare to the PV panel. Here the leakage energy of transformer is controlled by new decoupling circuit. So that there is no need to add extra dissipative circuits to decrease the power losses for improvement in efficiency.

Alian Chen et al. **[17]** have examined a new single-phase fly back based inverter. It is made up of a boost converter and a fly back inverter used for ac PV module schemes. For Boost converter, multilevel pulse train technique and DCM operation is utilized to produce a stable dc voltage. The output voltage ripple of the converter can be diminished successfully. Also aggregate capacitance on the dc-Link is decreased.

Shimizu, T. et al. **[18]** proposed a novel fly back-type inverter circuit topology appropriate for ac module structures. The high-frequency fly back transformer recognizes ac current injection into the utility line by reducing harmonic contents. A dc power smoothing circuit which is used to decrease low-frequency ripple voltage and a reduction in the total capacitance on the dc input side is offered in the paper. The electrolytic capacitors are exchanged by film capacitors of small capacitance. Subsequently, the matters related to short life period and large volume in micro inverter framework can be removed.

2.4 Summary

This chapter describes the overview of PV inverter system. Basic three topologies like central, string and micro inverter are presented. Out of all the three topologies, micro inverter has all the advantages and also overcome the disadvantages of central and string based inverters.

CHAPTER 3 DESIGN AND CIRCUIT ANALYSIS OF FLY BACK INVERTER

3.1   Introduction

The fly back topologies operate in a different way. During the power transistor "on" time, energy will be stored in the power transformer. During this period, the load current is supplied from an output filter capacitor only. When the power transistor turns "off," the energy stored in the power transformer is transferred to the load and to the output filter capacitor as it replaces the charge it lost when it only was sending load current.

The fly back has advantages and limitations. This is mostly valuable in low-cost multiple output power supplies yielding a significant saving in cost and space.

3.2   Basic fly back converter schematic and operation

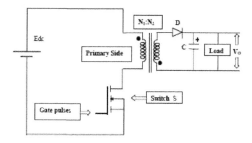

Figure 3. 1 Basic fly back converter schematic

From the circuit diagram of Fig.3.1, when switch 'S' is on, the primary winding of the transformer is connected to the input supply with its dotted end connected to the positive side. At the same time the diode 'D' connected in series with the secondary winding gets reverse biased because of the induced voltage in the secondary (dotted end potential being higher). Thus by the turning on of switch 'S', primary winding is

13

able to carry current but current in the secondary winding is blocked because of the reverse biased diode.

Fig.3.2 shows (in bold line) the current carrying part of the circuit and the circuit that is functionally equivalent to the fly-back circuit during 'on' period. In the equivalent circuit shown, the conducting switch or diode is taken as a shorted switch and the device that is not conducting is taken as an open switch.

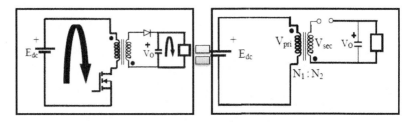

Figure 3. 2 Circuit operation when switch is 'on' and equivalent circuit

In fig.3.2, the value of primary voltage is E_{dc} and secondary voltage will be $V_{sec} = E_{dc} * \frac{N2}{N1}$.

$$V_{pri} = E_{dc} \tag{3.1}$$

$$V_{sec} = E_{dc} * \frac{N2}{N1} \tag{3.2}$$

At the end of switch-conduction, the energy stored in the magnetic field of the fly back inductor-transformer is equal to $L_{pri}I_p{}^2/2$, where I_p is the magnitude of primary current at the end of conduction period. Even if the secondary winding does not conduct during this mode, the load connected to the output capacitor gets uninterrupted current due to the previously stored charge on the capacitor.

When switch 'S' is turned off after conducting for some time, the primary winding current path is broken and according to laws of magnetic induction, the voltage polarities across the windings reverse. Reversal of voltage polarities makes the diode in the secondary circuit forward biased. Fig.3.3 shows the current path (in bold line) during 'off' period (left side) while right side one shows the functional equivalent of the circuit during this period.

14

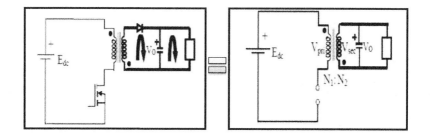

Figure 3. 3 Circuit operation when switch is 'off' and equivalent circuit

In fig.3.3, the value of primary voltage is $V_o * \frac{N2}{N1}$ and secondary voltage will be V_o.

$$V_{pri} = V_o * \frac{N2}{N1} \tag{3.3}$$

$$V_{sec} = V_o \tag{3.4}$$

3.3   Designing of transformer

The output Voltage requirement is 310Vm and input Voltage is 36 DC Volts. Thus the turn's ratio of transformer can be calculated using the value of output and input voltages,

$$\text{Turn's Ratio} = \frac{N2}{N1} = \frac{V_{out}}{V_{in}} = \frac{310}{36} = 8.61 \approx 9 \tag{3.5}$$

Step 1: Primary turns selected to satisfy the AC voltage stress and core AC saturation property.

$$N_p = \frac{VT}{BA_e} = \frac{V}{FBA_e} \tag{3.6}$$

Where, N_p= Minimum primary turns

V= Maximum primary DC voltage (36)

T= Maximum period for MOSFET (us)

F= Switching Frequency (50 kHz)

A_e= Effective centre pole area of the core

B= Magnetic flux swing typically 200mT

So by putting all values, we will get primary turns value N_p which is 0.37.

Step 2: find the value of primary inductance of coil wound on a core.

$$L_p = A_L N_p{}^2 \qquad (3.7)$$

Where, L_p = Primary inductance value

A_L= 3 µH for ETD34 core

N_p= Primary turns

By putting all values, we will get $L_p = 40\mu H$

Step 3: find the value of secondary inductance of coil wound on a core.

$$L_s = N^2 L_p \qquad (3.8)$$

Where, L_s = Secondary inductance value

N= Turns ratio (9)

L_p = Primary inductance value

By putting all values, we will get $L_s = 3.6\mu H$

3.4   Simulation of fly back type inverter

The above schematic shows the Pspice simulation diagram. Here voltage comparator LM311 is used; whose inputs are sine wave and triangular wave. Output of that comparator is given as gate signal to MOSFET. It is connected to primary winding of transformer. When switch (MOSFET) is "on", the energy will be stored and when it becomes "off", the energy will be delivered to secondary side. So, till now we have

16

rectified sine wave. At the end we have four switches, two for positive half cycle and two for negative half cycle. So now we have the sine wave of 310 volts peak to peak.

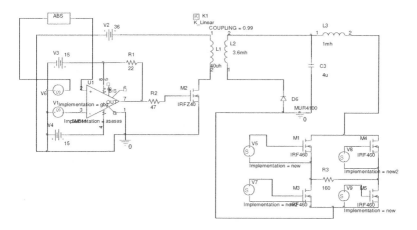

Figure 3. 4 Simulation circuit

3.4.1 Specifications of components

MOSFET IRF460:

Parameter	Value
Drain to source Voltage	$V_{DS} \geq 500V$
Drain current	$I_D = 21A$
Drain to source on state Resistance	$R_{DS} = 0.30 \, \Omega$

Table 3.1 Specifications of unfolder MOSFET

Diode MUR4100:

Parameter	Value
Maximum recurrent Peak Reverse Voltage	1000V

Maximum RMS Voltage	700V
Maximum DC Blocking Voltage	1000V
Maximum Reverse recovery Time	$T_{rr} = 75ns$

Table 3.2 Specifications of diode

Input MOSFET IRFZ40:

Parameter	Value
Drain to source Voltage	$V_{DS} = 50V$
Drain current	$I_D = 35A$
Drain to source on state Resistance	$R_{DS} = 0.028 \, \Omega$

Table 3.3 Specifications of input MOSFET

3.4.2 Specifications of the system

Parameter	Value
Power rating	300W
Input Voltage	36V
Output voltage	230 Vrms and 310 Vm
Switching Frequency	50kHz
Power Conversion Efficiency	96%
THD(Total Harmonic Distortion)	2.9%
Proposed DSP	TI TMS320F2X series
Simulation Tool	Pspice

Table 3.4 Specifications of the fly back type inverter system

3.5 Results

3.5.1 Gate drive pulses

The pulses for the inputs of last four switches are shown in fig.3.5 and fig 3.6. Switch M1 and M5 have same pulses (red one) and switch M3 and M4 have same pulses (green one) as input.

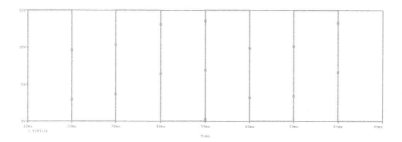

Figure 3. 5 Gate pulses for switches M3 and M4

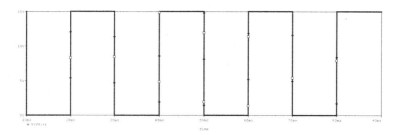

Figure 3. 6 Gate pulses for switches M1 and M5

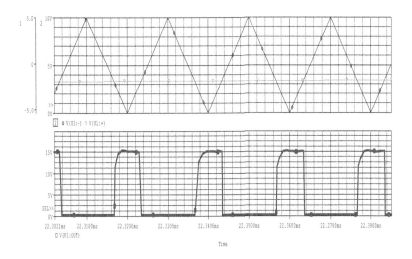

Figure 3. 7 SPWM generation for input MOSFET in Pspice

3.5.2 Voltage and current Waveforms

Fig.3.8 shows the input voltage waveforms, which shows 36V DC voltage.

Fig.3.9 shows the output voltage waveforms, which shows 310V AC sinusoidal waveforms.

Fig.3.10 shows the input current waveforms, which shows 8.5A and Fig.3.11 shows the output current waveforms, which shows 1.90A sinusoidal waveforms.

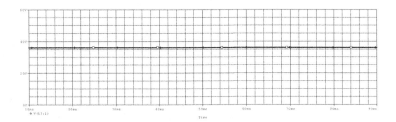

Figure 3. 8 Input voltage

20

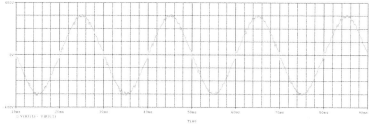

Figure 3. 9 Output voltage

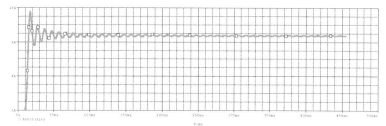

Figure 3. 10 Input current

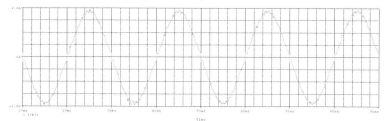

Figure 3. 11 Output current

3.5.3 FFT of output voltage

The graph shown in fig.3.12 represents the Fast Fourier Transform (FFT) of the output voltage. The frequency component at 50Hz which is fundamental frequency component with some small harmonics are shown. The second harmonic component is at 150Hz. The calculation for total harmonic distortion (THD) is estimated as,

$$\text{THD} = \frac{\sqrt{\sum_{h=2}^{\infty}(V_h)^2}}{V_1} \quad = 2.9\% \tag{3.8}$$

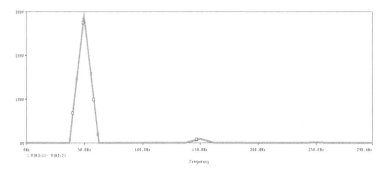

Figure 3. 12 FFT graph of output voltage

3.5.4 Loss analysis

Fig.3.13 shows zoomed vision of the switching loss and conduction loss for unfolder MOSFET (H Bridge 4 MOSFETs) and fig.3.14 shows the switching loss and conduction loss for input switch and over one switching cycle. These figures represent the integrated loss found by integration of the instantaneous power loss in the circuit.

Simulation results provide complete estimate of losses in the switches (MOSFETs). The losses are depends on the model parameters of the parts presented in PsPice. Table 3.5 shows the total loss estimate of all the switches from above discussion.

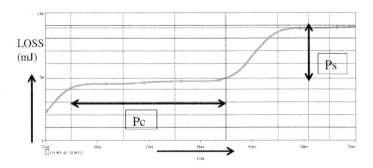

Figure 3. 13 Switching and conduction Losses of H bridge switches

22

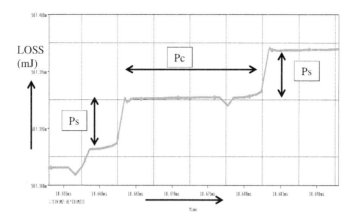

Figure 3. 14 Switching and conduction losses of input switch

The total loss calculation is shown in following Table 3.5.

Input MOSFET Switching Loss	0.75W
Input MOSFET Conduction Loss	0.85W
Unfolder Switching Loss	(0.4*4)= 1.6W
Unfolder Conduction Loss	(0.8*4)= 3.2W
Total Loss	6.55W

Table 3.5 Total loss analysis of fly back type inverter

3.5.5 Power calculation

The output Power requirement is 300W (Pout=300W). So that output resistance value calculated using following formula,

$$R = \frac{V^2}{P} = \frac{220^2}{300} = 160 \text{ ohm} \tag{3.9}$$

The input Current is 6.18A and input Voltage is 36 volts. The input Power can be calculated as,

$$P_{in} = V_{in} * I_{in} = 36 * 8.5 = 306 \text{ W} \tag{3.10}$$

The value of output Voltage from simulation results is 236 Vm. So the value of output Power can be calculated as,

$$P_{out} = \frac{Vout}{\sqrt{2}} * \frac{Iout}{\sqrt{2}} = (310*1.91)/2 = 296.05 \text{ W} \tag{3.11}$$

The efficiency can be calculated using value of output power and input power simply by taking the ratio of both values,

$$\eta = \frac{Pout}{Pin} = \frac{296.05}{306} = 0.9674 = 96.74 \text{ \%} \tag{3.12}$$

The efficiency of proposed inverter topology is nearer to 97%

3.6 Summary

This chapter describes the proposed fly back type inverter. It has transformer which provides isolation and also used for boosting the input voltage by selecting turns ratio of it. Here only one switch at input side with SPWM is used for switching and control of inverter, which makes this circuit very simple and cost efficient. It has capability to reduce the effect of shadows at panel side. It gives the grid synchronous sine wave. Table 3.6 shows the analytical comparison of existing and proposed fly back type inverter.

Parameter	Fly back	Proposed Fly back
Input voltage	25-38 V	36 V
Output voltage	220 V	220 V
Output power	195 W	296 W
Switching frequency	40 kHz	50 kHz
MOSFET count for controlling purpose	2	1
FFT (fundamental frequency)	50 Hz	50 Hz

Table 3.6 Analytical comparison of existing fly back and proposed fly back

24

CHAPTER 4 DESIGN AND CIRCUIT ANALYSIS OF ISOLATED FULL BRIDGE INVERTER

4.1 Introduction

The input voltage of one PV panel is very low for micro-inverter; voltage gain should be increased for connection with single phase system. A transformer less design has certain limitations to amplify the voltage up to utility level. A voltage gain and isolation is given by high frequency transformer. Single phase arrangement shown in fig.4.1, which is single stage bridge micro inverter topology with isolation. Gate drive signal for primary or the main bridge is SPWM. Isolation between PV panel and the output load is given by the transformer. The output of the transformer is given to rectifier diodes and then it is followed by filter and an unfolder bridge.

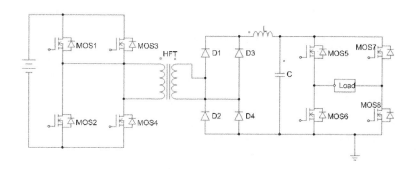

Figure 4. 1 Block diagram of isolated full bridge inverter

From fig.4.1, when MOS1 and MOS4 are ON (with MOS2 and MOS3 OFF), current will pass through high frequency transformer, switches MOS2 and MOS3 will be ON for next cycle because the drive signal of both the diagonal leg are opposite of each other. When MOS2 and MOS3 will ON (M1 and M4 OFF), the current will pass through high frequency transformer. Thus, transformer will not float in negative cycle and it will reset properly. According to turn's ratio, high frequency low voltage, high current dc pulses are amplified to high voltage, low current ac pulses at the secondary

25

output of the transformer. The diode rectifier consisting of D1-D4 converts this high frequency high magnitude ac signal to rectified sinusoidal voltage having line frequency envelope. An LC filter is used to eliminate the high frequency modulation and produce the rectified output. Proper corner frequency must be chosen to provide adequate filtration at very high frequency. An unfolder bridge circuit is switched diagonally at line frequency (50Hz) to produce utility grid voltage 220 Vrms with 50 Hz frequency.

4.2   Designing of transformer

The output Voltage requirement is 310Vm and input Voltage is 36 DC Volts. Thus the turn's ratio of transformer can be calculated using the value of output and input voltages,

$$\text{Turn's Ratio} = \frac{N2}{N1} = \frac{V_{out}}{V_{in}} = \frac{310}{36} = 8.61 \approx 9 \qquad (4.1)$$

Step 1: Primary turns selected to satisfy the AC voltage stress and core AC saturation property.

$$N_p = \frac{VT}{BA_e} = \frac{V}{FBA_e} \qquad (4.2)$$

Where, N_p= Minimum primary turns

V= Maximum primary DC voltage (36)

T= Maximum period for MOSFET (us)

F= Switching Frequency (50 kHz)

A_e= Effective centre pole area of the core

B= Magnetic flux swing typically 200mT

So by putting all values, we will get primary turns value N_p which is 0.37.

Step 2: find the value of primary inductance of coil wound on a core.

$$L_p = A_L N_p{}^2 \qquad (4.3)$$

26

Where, L_p = Primary inductance value

A_L= 3 μH for ETD34 core

N_p= Primary turns

By putting all values, we will get $L_p = 40$μH

Step 3: find the value of secondary inductance of coil wound on a core.

$$L_s = N^2 L_p \qquad (4.4)$$

Where, L_s = Secondary inductance value

N= Turns ratio (9)

L_p = Primary inductance value

By putting all values, we will get $L_s = 3.6$μH

4.4 Simulation of isolated full bridge type inverter

The schematic shown in fig.4.2 is Pspice simulation diagram. Here voltage comparator LM311 is used; whose inputs are sine wave and triangular wave. Output of that comparator is given as gate signal to all MOSFETs of full bridge. The full bridge comprises of four switches M1-M4 which are switched diagonally. The switches M1-M4 is one diagonal leg and switches M2-M3 is treated as the other diagonal leg of the bridge. Gate drive signals for bridge MOSFETs are sinusoidal pulse width modulated (SPWM), which are generated from comparator.

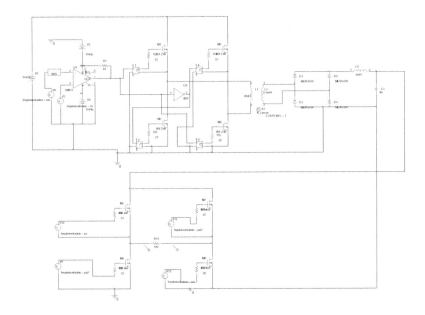

Figure 4. 2 Simulation circuit of isolated full bridge inverter

The positive half cycled sinusoidal signal with frequency of 50 Hz is compared with high frequency triangular carrier signal for generating sinusoidal pulse width modulated (SPWM) driving pulses for one diagonal of bridge (M1-M4) of the main bridge. And inverted SPWM is given to the other diagonal (M2-M3). If the switching frequency of triangular wave is f_s, then the time period will be $T_s = \frac{1}{f_s}$.

From fig.4.2, when switches M1 and M4 are ON (with M2 and M3 OFF), current will pass over high frequency transformer, switches M2 and M3 will be ON for next cycle because the drive signal of both the diagonal leg are opposite of each other. When M2 and M3 will ON (M1 and M4 OFF), the current will pass through high frequency transformer. Thus, transformer will not drift in negative cycle and it will reset properly. Based on the turn's ratio, high frequency, low voltage, and high current dc pulses are enlarged to low current and high voltage ac pulses at the secondary side of the transformer. The diode rectifier includes D1-D4 diodes to convert this high frequency and high amplitude ac signal to rectified sinusoidal voltage having line frequency. Inductor-capacitor filter is required to remove the high frequency

28

modulation and produce the rectified output signal. Appropriate corner frequency need to be selected to offer suitable filtration at high frequency. An unfolder bridge circuit is used to make rectified sine wave to pure sine wave with amplitude of 220 V_{rms} and 50 Hz frequency by switching bridge MOSFTEs diagonally. So now we have the sine wave of 310 volts peak to peak.

4.4.1 Specifications of components

MOSFET IRF460:

Parameter	Value
Drain to source Voltage	$V_{DS} \geq 500V$
Drain current	$I_D = 21A$
Drain to source on state Resistance	$R_{DS} = 0.30\ \Omega$

Table 4.1 Specifications of unfolder MOSFET

Diode MUR4100:

Parameter	Value
Maximum recurrent Peak Reverse Voltage	1000V
Maximum RMS Voltage	700V
Maximum DC Blocking Voltage	1000V
Maximum Reverse recovery Time	$T_{rr} = 75ns$

Table 4.2 Specifications of rectifier Diode

Input MOSFET IRFZ40:

Parameter	Value

29

Drain to source Voltage	$V_{DS} = 50V$
Drain current	$I_D = 35A$
Drain to source on state Resistance	$R_{DS} = 0.028 \, \Omega$

Table 4.3 Specifications of input MOSFET

4.4.2 Specifications of the system

Parameter	Value
Power rating	300 W
Input Voltage	36 V
Output voltage	230 Vrms and 310 Vm
Switching Frequency	100 kHz
Power Conversion Efficiency	97%
THD(Total Harmonic Distortion)	2.01%
Proposed DSP	TI TMS320F2X series
Simulation Tool	Pspice

Table 4.4 Specification of the isolated full bridge type inverter system

4.5　Results

4.5.1　Gate drive pulses

The pulses for the inputs of last four switches are shown in fig.4.3 and fig.4.4. Switch M5 and M8 have same pulses (pink one) and switch M6 and M7 have same pulses (blue one) as input.

Fig.4.5 shows the sinusoidal pulse width modulated (SPWM) for one diagonal leg of input bridge MOSFETs.

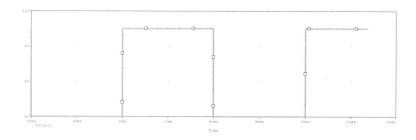

Figure 4. 3 Gate pulses for switches M5 and M8

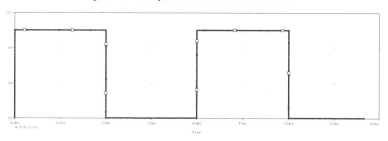

Figure 4. 4 Gate pulses for switches M6 and M7

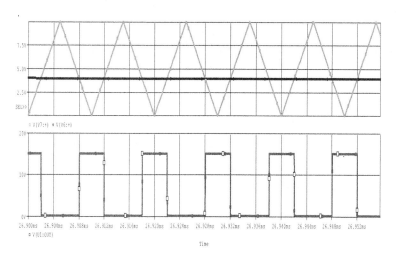

Figure 4. 5 SPWM generations for input MOSFETs in Pspice

31

4.5.2 Voltage and current waveforms

Fig.4.6 shows the input voltage waveforms, which shows 36V DC voltage.

Fig.4.7 shows the output voltage waveforms, which shows 310V AC sinusoidal waveforms.

Fig.4.8 shows the input current waveforms, which shows 8.5A and Fig.4.9 shows the output current waveforms, which shows 1.90A sinusoidal waveforms.

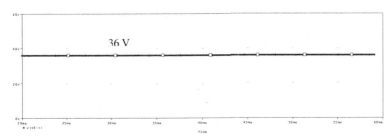

Figure 4. 6 Input voltage

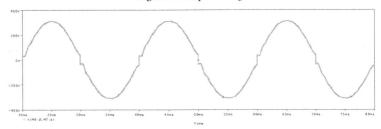

Figure 4. 7 Output voltage

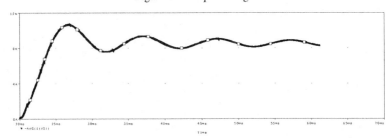

Figure 4. 8 Input current

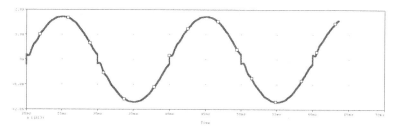

Figure 4. 9 Output current

4.5.3 FFT of output voltage

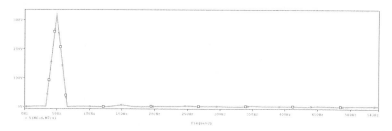

Figure 4. 10 FFT graph of output voltage

This graph shown in fig.4.11 represents the Fast Fourier Transform (FFT) of the output voltage (310 V). The frequency component at 50Hz is marked which fundamental frequency with some small harmonics. The second harmonic component is at 150Hz. The calculation for total harmonic distortion (THD) is as follows,

$$\text{THD} = \frac{\sqrt{\sum_{h=2}^{\infty}(V_h)^2}}{V_1} = 2.01\% \tag{4.5}$$

4.5.4 Loss analysis

Fig.4.11 displays zoomed vision of the conduction losses and switching losses of unfolder MOSFETs (H Bridge 4 MOSFETs) and fig.4.12 shows the conduction losses and switching losses of input switches over one switching cycle. These figures represent the integrated loss found by integration of the instantaneous power loss in the circuit. Simulation provides detailed prediction of losses in the semiconductor switches (MOSFETs). These losses are based on the model constraints of the parts given in PsPice.

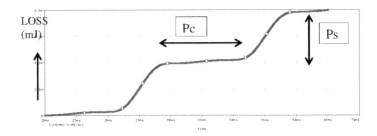

Figure 4. 11 Switching and conduction Losses of H bridge switches

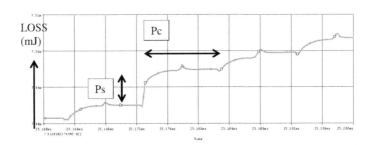

Figure 4. 12 Switching and conduction losses of input switches

Table 4.5 shows the total loss budget from the discussion.

Input MOSFET Switching and conduction Loss	2W
Unfolder Switching and conduction Loss	(0.1635*4)= 0.65W
Total Loss	2.65W

Table 4.5 Total loss analysis of isolated full bridge type inverter

34

4.5.5 Power calculation

The output Power requirement is 270W (Pout=270W). So that output resistance value calculated using following formula,

$$R = \frac{V^2}{P} = \frac{220^2}{270} = 180 \text{ ohm} \qquad (4.6)$$

The input Current is 6.18A and input Voltage is 36 volts. The input Power can be calculated as,

$$P_{in} = V_{in} * I_{in} = 36 * 7.5 = 270 \text{ W} \qquad (4.7)$$

The value of output Voltage from simulation results is 236 Vm. So the value of output Power can be calculated as,

$$P_{out} = \frac{Vout}{\sqrt{2}} * \frac{Iout}{\sqrt{2}} = (310*1.7)/2 = 263.5 \text{ W} \qquad (4.8)$$

The efficiency can be calculated using value of output power and input power simply by taking the ratio of both values,

$$\eta = \frac{Pout}{Pin} = \frac{263.5}{270} = 0.9759 = 97.59 \text{ \%} \qquad (4.9)$$

The efficiency of proposed inverter topology is nearer to 97 %.

4.5 Summary

In this chapter isolated full bridge PV micro-inverter topology is presented with better efficiency. This topology gives the necessary larger output voltage compared to input voltage based on selected turns ratio of the transformer. The advantages of this isolated full bridge inverter are: (1) Four switches in the bridge with SPWM drive pulses are used for controlling and switching purpose of inverter, (2) very modest design with less complexity and (3) efficiency is projected as 97%, at switching frequency of 100 kHz.

The proposed topology for inverter is isolated full bridge type inverter. It has transformer which provides isolation. It gives the grid synchronous sine wave with fundamental frequency 50Hz. Table shows the analytical comparison of existing full bridge and proposed full bridge type inverter system.

Parameter	Old full bridge	Proposed Isolated Full bridge
Input voltage	12	36
Turns ratio	1:53	1:9
Controller/DSP	PIC controller	DSP TMS320F28335
PWM method	Normal PWM	Sinusoidal PWM
Switching frequency	20 kHz	100 kHz

Table 4.6 Analytical comparison of existing full bridge and proposed full bridge type inverter system

CHAPTER 5 SPWM GENERATION USING DSP

5.1 SPWM generation using DSP TMS320F28335

Sinusoidal pulse width modulated (SPWM) includes sine wave as a reference signal and triangular wave as a carrier signal. This model for SPWM uses the ePWM (Enhanced Pulse Width Modulation) parts of the Event Manager Modules given in the DSP to produce PWM pulses. Drive signals which is SPWM, used in this project includes sine wave as the reference signal, is outwardly given as the compare value. Triangular pulses which are modulating signals, generated inside the ePWM block of Event Manager Module of the DSP by giving the appropriate values.

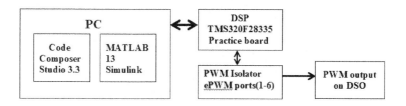

Figure 5. 1 Block diagram of SPWM switching pulse generation using DSP

5.1.1 Simulink model for SPWM

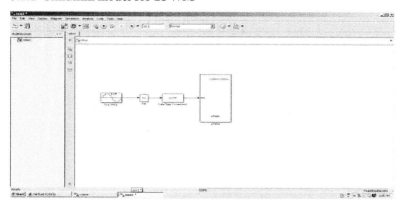

Figure 5. 2 Simulink model for SPWM

This model includes sine wave block that is being compared with sawtooth wave which is internally generated in ePWM block by setting parameter of it.

Now Sine block parameters are selected for frequency 50Hz and amplitude value is half of the timer period value which is selected in ePWM block parameter.

The ePWM block consists timer period value which selected as per equation shown below

$$TxPR = \frac{CPU\ Clock\ Frequency}{Desired\ Frequency(Switching\ Frequency)} = \frac{150\ MHz}{50kHz} = 3000 \qquad (5.1)$$

The counting mode is selected as per user's requirement; here it is selected as Up counting mode. For one SPWM generation, we require only on ePWM module so we need to select ePWM1A. Both the Sink and Source Blocks are shown in fig 5.3.

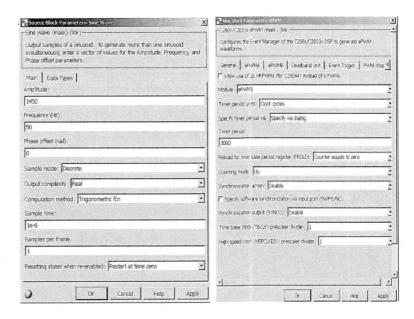

Figure 5. 3 Source block (Sine wave) and sink block (ePWM) parameter

38

5.1.2 Configuration Parameter

For building this model, configuration parameter need to be set.

Step 1: Settings (Configuration Parameter) ⟶ Hardware implementation

For DSP F28335 kit, we need to select device vendor as Texas instruments and Device type as C2000.

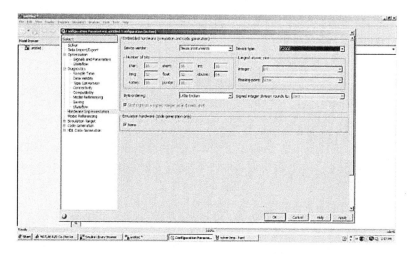

Figure 5. 4 Hardware implementation in configuration parameter

Step 2: Settings (Configuration Parameter) ⟶Code generation

In code generation, we need to select system target file as "idelink_ert.tlc" as shown in fig.5.5.

Figure 5. 5 Code generation tab in configuration parameter for selection of system target file

Step 3: Settings (Configuration Parameter) ——>Code generation——>Coder Target

In coder target, we need to select IDE/tool chain as Texas Instruments Code Composer Studio and board properties are selected for board F28335 as shown in fig 5.6.

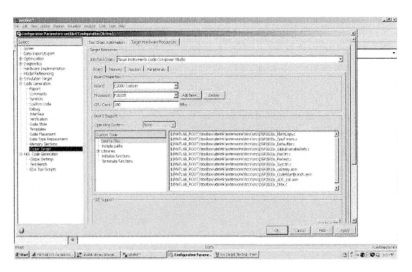

Figure 5. 6 Coder target in configuration parameter

5.2 DSP TMS320F28335 kit Connection with PWM isolator Board

DSP EPB28335 consists ePWM module and the EPB28335 has an RS-232 connector which brings out the PWM signals. The RS-232 connector is connected to ASK-30_PWM Isolator and output is taken from port 1 of ASK-30_PWM Isolator at pin no 1.

Figure 5. 7 Practice board of DSP F28335

The ASK30 is a general-purpose PWM isolator which outputs +15V DC isolated PWM from +5V DC PWM input waveform. The board is designed to be a flexible platform for developing inverter application. Power and all signals needed for a controller are available on the board, giving a modular system where boards with different microcontrollers/DSPs can easily be connected.

Figure 5. 8 PWM isolator module

The fig.5.9 shows the connection of practice board and PWM isolator board. In PWM isolator board, 6 ePWM ports are available. Out of them, only ePWM 1 is used for generating SPWM out of it. Pins of ePWM are connected to the probes of DSO to show the SPWM on DSO.

PWM1AB Connector (PL2):

Figure 5. 9 Practice board and PWM isolator module connection

Pin specification for PWM 1A-1B port (in figure yellow circle) are shown in Table 5.1

Pin Number	Pin Detail
1	PWM1A
2	PWM1B
3	Error
4	15 V
5	GND

Table 5.1 Pin specification for PWM 1A-1B port

The fig.5.10 represents complete setup of DSP module with MATLAB-CCS running in PC for generation of SPWM. MATLAB Simulink model is internally connected to CCS 3.3 then CCS will interface with DSP practice board and board is connected to PWM isolator board via RS-232 connector. Then DSO probes are connected at the ePWM1 port pins.

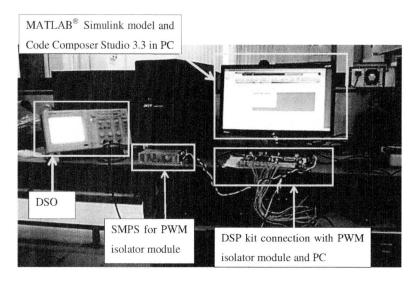

Figure 5. 10 Complete setup for SPWM generation using DSP

5.2.1 Output of SPWM

Here the output SPWM is of 50 Khz and The variation in the width of pulses shows variation in amplitude of sine wave.

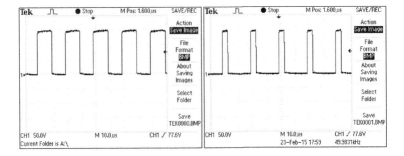

Figure 5. 11 SPWM on DSO with 50 kHz

5.3 Simulink model of PWM generation for unfolder

Two GPIO output pins are allocated for generation of PWM for unfolder. The output of sine wave is given to MATLAB function for simultaneous generation of PWM.

MATLAB function:

if u>0   %if sine wave has positive amplitude

y1=1;y2=0;

Else   %if sine wave has positive amplitude

y1=0;y2=1;

end

44

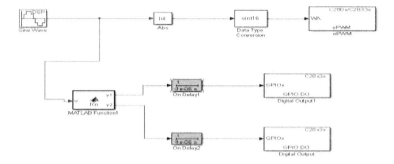

Figure 5. 12 Simulink model for PWM generation for unfolder

5.3.1 Output of PWM

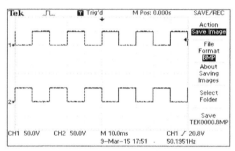

Figure 5. 13 PWM with 50 Hz

5.4 Proposed DSP system

Features of DSP 28335 are listed below:

❖ High-Performance Static CMOS Technology

- 150 Mhz. Max operating speed

❖ High-Performance 32-Bit CPU (TMS320C28x)

- IEEE-754 Single-Precision Floating-Point

- Unit (FPU) (F2833x only)

- 16 x 16 and 32 x 32 MAC Operations

- 16 x 16 Dual MAC

- Harvard Bus Architecture
- Fast Interrupt Response and Processing

❖ Enhanced Control Peripherals

- Up to 18 PWM Outputs
- Up to 6 HRPWM Outputs With 150 ps MEP
- Up to 6 Event Capture Inputs
- Up to 2 Quadrature Encoder Interfaces
- Up to 8 32-Bit/Nine 16-Bit Timers

❖ Three 32-Bit CPU Timers

❖ 12-Bit ADC, 16 Channels

❖ Up to 88 Individually Programmable Multiplexed GPIO Pins with Input Filtering

❖ JTAG Boundary Scan Support

❖ Advanced Emulation Features

- Analysis and Breakpoint Functions
- Real-Time Debug via Hardware

❖ Development Support Includes

- ANSI C/C++ Compiler/Assembler/Linker
- Code Composer Studio™ IDE
- DSP/BIOS™
- Clock and System Control
- Dynamic PLL Ratio Changes Supported
- On-Chip Oscillator
- Watchdog Timer Module

❖ Low-Power Modes and Power Savings

- IDLE, STANDBY, HALT Modes Supported Supports All 58 Peripheral Interrupt

46

- Disable Individual Peripheral Clocks

5.5 Conclusion

The DSP based converter offers a fast response improving the system reliability. Hardware circuitry or microcontroller is less accurate and most of the solar energy cannot be converted into electrical energy. We need many microcontrollers to control converter and inverter in PV system. But single DSP can control both converter and inverter.

DSP based generation of SPWM is very accurate and can be generated without writing long codes. It requires generating a model in Simulink (MATLAB) and by setting configuration parameter related to DSP which is being used.

CHAPTER 6 DESIGN OF TEST PROTOTYPE

6.1 Introduction

Analysis of the inverter is done by using simulation and investigation. This chapter includes the simulation circuit and results of this experimentation are presented. Also, the drive signal generation for MOSFETs is presented. The circuit for experimentation is displayed in fig.6.1

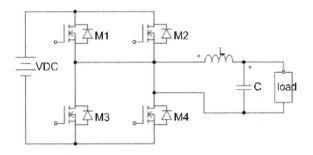

Figure 6. 1 Basic full bridge circuit

6.2 Simulation of proposed circuit

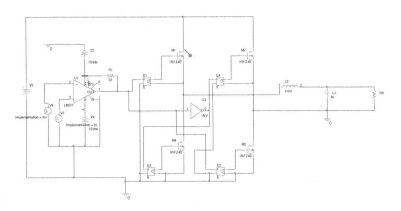

Figure 6. 2 Simulation of full bridge circuit

As shown in figure, the gate pulse for all four MOSFET are sinusoidal pulse width modulated (SPWM). The switching frequency of 10 kHz triangular wave is being compared with sine wave of 50 Hz by using comparator. Than the output SPWM is given to one diagonal leg of bridge (e.g. M1 and M3). And inverted SPWM is given to another diagonal leg of bridge (e.g. M2 and M4). The LC filter is connected across the bridge circuit with suitable cut off frequency. The output voltage is measured across load resistor.

6.3 Simulation results

6.3.1 Voltage and current waveforms

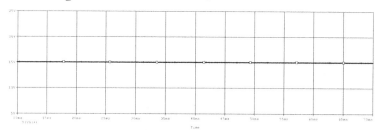

Figure 6. 3 Input voltage

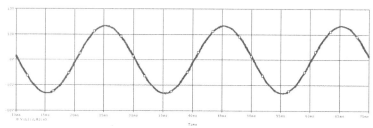

Figure 6. 4 Output voltage

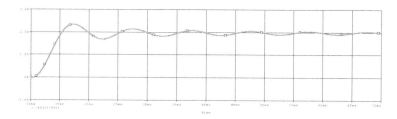

Figure 6. 5 Input current

49

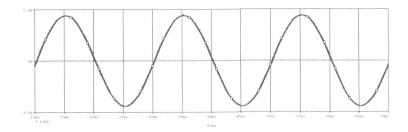

Figure 6. 6 Output Current

6.3.2 Power calculation

The output Power requirement is 30W (Pout=30W). So that output resistance value calculated using following formula,

$$R = \frac{V^2}{P} = \frac{14^2}{2*30} = 7\text{ohm} \qquad (6.1)$$

The input Current is 2A and input Voltage is 15 volts. The input Power can be calculated as,

$$P_{in} = V_{in} * I_{in} = 15*2 = 30 \text{ W} \qquad (6.2)$$

The value of output Voltage from simulation results is 13 Vm. So the value of output Power can be calculated as,

$$P_{out} = \frac{Vout}{\sqrt{2}} * \frac{Iout}{\sqrt{2}} = (13*4.4)/2 = 28.6\text{W} \qquad (6.3)$$

The efficiency can be calculated using value of output power and input power simply by taking the ratio of both values,

$$\eta = \frac{Pout}{Pin} = \frac{28.6}{30} = 0.9533 = 95.33 \text{ \%} \qquad (6.4)$$

The efficiency of proposed inverter topology is nearer to 95%.

6.4   Hardware prototype

6.3.1 SPWM generation for bridge MOSFETs

The bridge circuit includes four MOSFETs. Sinusoidal pulse width modulated (SPWM) for these MOSFETs are generated using DSP TMS320F28335. MATLAB Simulink model is created in MATLAB and then it is internally connected with code composer studio 3.3. Then PC (computer) is directly connected to DSP kit. And DSP kit is connected with PWM isolator module. That module includes ePWM ports, by connecting DSO probes to this port pins we can get SPWM on DSO for testing purpose. Then that port pins are directly connected to bridge MOSFETs. Fig 6.8 shows the DSO test results for both diagonal of bridge MOSFETs. Upper one (green) pulses is for one diagonal (e.g.M1 and M3) and yellow pulses, which is inverted version of green pulses is for another diagonal (e.g.M2 and M4).

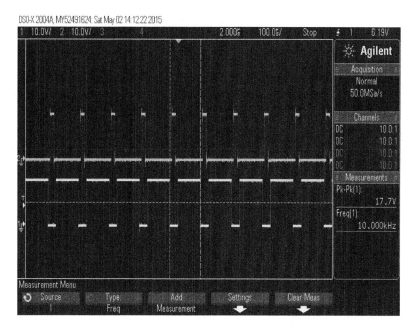

Figure 6. 7 SPWM for bridge MOSFTEs

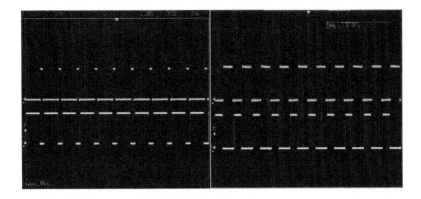

Figure 6. 8 SPWM for MOSFETs

6.4.2 Setup of proposed system

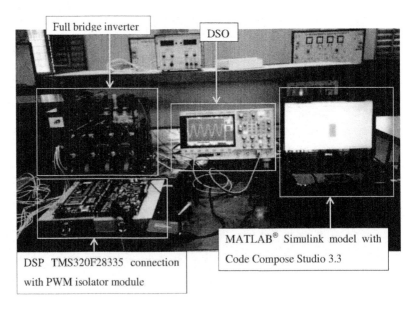

Figure 6. 9 Laboratory prototype

Fig.6.9 shows the laboratory setup of stand-alone power generation module, which includes full bridge inverter, the drive pulses (SPWM) from DSP TMS320F28335 kit and DSO. Here because of limited availability of resources, we have made simple laboratory prototype which includes available full bridge inverter and DSP kit for generation of sinusoidal pulse width modulated signals for gate drive pulses of switches used in full bridge circuit. MATLAB and code composer studio 3.3 (CCS 3.3) is internally connected. Then CCS will provide a path for connection with DSP practice board. Finally the output SPWM is fed to the switches of full bridge inverter and the inverter output is shown in DSO which is sine wave with 220 V and 50 Hz.

6.5 Conclusion

An experimental setup of planned micro inverter has been designed, simulated and analysed experimentally. The simulation results and laboratory prototype's experimental results show that the suggested micro-inverter has better power conversion efficiency with simple circuit.

CHAPTER 7 CONCLUSIONS AND FUTURE PLAN

7.1 Conclusions

- When a some modules are partially covered by shadows, centralized inverter and string inverter can't work. So the solution is to use AC module/micro inverter, in which each panel has its own built in inverter. By employing micro inverter in the stand alone power generation system, higher efficiency can be achieved as it avoids the shadow effects.

- In micro inverters, proposed fly back inverter has very simple architecture and very cost effective. Fly back inverter also provides isolation via transformer. It controls the whole inverter by using only one switch at the input.

- Isolated full bridge inverter with sinusoidal pulse width modulated (SPWM) gate drive pulses provides very good result compare to existing PWM based full bridge inverter.

- SPWM gate drive pulses are generated using DSP, which gives accurate results. Generation of SPWM by using DSP via MATLAB-CCS interconnection provides better output than writing long codes for generation of SPWM and gives simpler connections.

- By using SPWM as a date drive pulses, full bridge circuit improves its quality such as smooth output voltage-current waveform than only PWM technique. Given laboratory setup for stand-alone power generation module is very simple with better results compared to PWM based inverters.

7.2 Future plan

This micro inverter topology can be used for higher power requirement by connecting all such small modules in series.

REFERENCES

[1] M. Calais, J. Myrzik, T. Spooner, and V. G. Agelidis, "Inverters for single-phase grid connected photovoltaic systems—An overview," in *Proc. IEEE PESC'02*, vol. 2, 2002, pp. 1995–2000.

[2] S. B. Kjaer, J. K. Pedersen, and F. Blaabjerg, "Power inverter topologies for photovoltaic modules—A review," in *Conf. Rec. IEEE-IAS Annu. Meeting*, vol. 2, 2002, pp. 782–788

[3] Y. Xue, L. Chang, S. B. Kjaer, J. Bordonau, and T. Shimizu, "Topologies of single-phase inverters for small distributed power generators: an overview," *IEEE Trans. Power Electron.*, vol. 19, no. 5, pp. 1305–1314, Sep. 2004.

[4] Soeren BaekhoejKjaer, John K. Pedersen and FredeBlaabjerg, "A Review of Single-Phase Grid-Connected Inverters for Photovoltaic Modules," *IEEE Transactions on Industry Applications*, vol. 41, No. 5, Sept-Oct 2005

[5] Toshihisa Shimizu, Keiji Wada, Naoki Nakamura, "AFlyback-type Single Phase Utility Interactive Inverter with Low-frequency Ripple Current Reduction on the DC Input for an AC Photovoltaic Module System," in *Proc. IEEE PESC'02*, Cairns, Australia, June 23–27, 2002, pp. 1483-1488.

[6] S. B. Kjaer and F. Blaabjerg,"Design optimization of a single phase inverter for photovoltaic applications," in *Proc. IEEE PESC'03*, vol. 3, 2003, pp. 1183–1190

[7] Abdel-Rahim, O.; Orabi, M.; Ahmed, M.E., "Development of high-gain high-efficiency grid-connected inverter for PV Module," Power Electronics for Distributed Generation Systems (PEDG), 2010 2nd IEEE International Symposium on , vol., no., pp.368,373, 16-18 June 2010

[8] T. Shimizu, O. Hashimoto, and G. Kimura, "A novel high-performance utility-interactive photovoltaic inverter system," *IEEE Trans. Power Electron.*, vol. 18, no. 2, pp. 704–711, Mar. 2003.

[9] T. Shimizu, M. Hirakata, T. Kamezawa, and H. Watanabe, "Generation control circuit for photovoltaic modules," *IEEE Trans. Power Electron.*, vol. 16, no. 3, pp. 293–300, May 2001.

[10] Yu Fang and Xudong Ma," A Novel PV Micro inverter With Coupled Inductors and Double-Boost Topology," *IEEE Transactions on power electronics*, VOL. 25, NO. 12, DECEMBER 2010-8

[11] Xiaonan Lu; Kai Sun; Yiwei Ma; Lipei Huang; Igarashi, S., "High efficiency hybrid cascade inverter for photovoltaic generation," TENCON 2009 - 2009 IEEE Region 10 Conference , vol., no., pp.1,6, 23-26 Jan. 2009

[12] Erickson, R.W.; Rogers, A.P., "A Micro-inverter for Building-Integrated Photovoltaics," Applied Power Electronics Conference and Exposition, 2009. APEC 2009. Twenty-Fourth Annual IEEE , vol., no., pp.911,917, 15-19 Feb. 2009

[13] Joshi, M.; Shoubaki, E.; Amarin, R.; Modick, B.; Enslin, J., "A high-efficiency resonant solar micro-inverter," Power Electronics and Applications (EPE 2011), Proceedings of the 2011-14th European Conference on , vol., no., pp.1,10, Aug. 30 2011-Sept. 1 2011

[14] Abdel-Rahim, O.; Orabi, M.; Ahmed, M.E., "High gain single-stage inverter for photovoltaic AC modules," Applied Power Electronics Conference and Exposition (APEC), 2011 Twenty-Sixth Annual IEEE , vol., no., pp.1961,1967, 6-11 March 2011

[15] *Mohammad Kamil,"* Grid-Connected Solar Microinverter Reference Design Using a dsPIC® Digital Signal Controller," *Microchip Technology Inc.*

[16] Haibing Hu; Harb, S.; Kutkut, N.H.; Shen, Z.J.; Batarseh, I., "A Single-Stage Microinverter Without Using Eletrolytic Capacitors," Power Electronics, IEEE Transactions on , vol.28, no.6, pp.2677,2687, June 2013

[17] Alian Chen; Shao Daming; Du Chunshui; Chenghui Zhang, "High-frequency DC link flyback single phase inverter for grid-connected photovoltaic system," Power Electronics for Distributed Generation Systems (PEDG), 2010 2nd IEEE International Symposium on , vol., no., pp.364,367, 16-18 June 2010

[18] Shimizu, T.; Wada, K.; Nakamura, N., "Flyback-Type Single-Phase Utility Interactive Inverter With Power Pulsation Decoupling on the DC Input for an AC Photovoltaic Module System," Power Electronics, IEEE Transactions on , vol.21, no.5, pp.1264,1272, Sept. 2006

[19] Pragallapati, N.; Agarwal, V., "Single phase solar PV module integrated flyback based micro-inverter with novel active power decoupling," Power Electronics,

Machines and Drives (PEMD 2014), 7th IET International Conference on , vol., no., pp.1,6, 8-10 April 2014

[20] Edwin, F.; Weidong Xiao; Khadkikar, V., "Topology review of single phase grid-connected module integrated converters for PV applications," IECON 2012 - 38th Annual Conference on IEEE Industrial Electronics Society , vol., no., pp.821,827, 25-28 Oct. 2012

[21] S. B. Kær and F. Blaabjerg, "A novel single-stage inverter for the ac-module with reduced low-frequency ripple penetration," in *Proc. 10th EPE European Conf. Power Electronics and Applications*,Toulouse, France, Sept. 2–4, 2003.

[22] Trubitsyn, A.; Pierquet, B.J.; Hayman, A.K.; Gamache, G.E.; Sullivan, C.R.; Perreault, D.J., "High-efficiency inverter for photovoltaic applications," Energy Conversion Congress and Exposition (ECCE), 2010 IEEE , vol., no., pp.2803,2810, 12-16 Sept. 2010

[23] Tan KhengKwang; Masri, S., "Single phase grid tie inverter for photovoltaic application," Sustainable Utilization and Development in Engineering and Technology (STUDENT), 2010 IEEE Conference on , vol., no., pp.23,28, 20-21 Nov. 2010

[24] Nanakos, A.C.; Tatakis, E.C.; Dimitrakakis, G.S.; Papanikolaou, N.P.; Kyritsis, A.C., "A novel design methodology maximizing the weighted-efficiency of flyback inverter for AC photovoltaic modules," Power Electronics and Applications (EPE 2011), Proceedings of the 2011-14th European Conference on , vol., no., pp.1,10, Aug. 30 2011-Sept. 1 2011

[25] Chun-Yu Yang; Yu-Chen Chang; Chia-Hsing Li; Shih-Jen Cheng; Qi-Ming Huang; Ching-Chun Chuang; Huang-Jen Chiu; Yu-Kang Lo; Min-ChienKuo; Yi-Ming Huang; Yuan-Bor Jean; Yung-Cheng Huang, "A module-integrated isolated solar micro-inverter," Industrial Informatics (INDIN), 2012 10th IEEE International Conference on , vol., no., pp.780,785, 25-27 July 2012

[26] Abraham I. Pressman, Keith Billings, Taylor Morcy, "Switching power supply Design" Third Edition.

[27] DSP TMS320F28335 datasheet

Printed in Great Britain
by Amazon